# Little Bird

Written by Guadalupe V. Lopez
Illustrated by Annie Lunsford

Scott Foresman

Look at my house.

I like my house.

I am a little bird.

My mom is a big bird.

It is fun to be a little bird.

I can play in the water.

I see my mom fly to

our house.

I can fly to our house.

Mom and I like our house.